Get to the heart of Biology with CGP!

There's a lot to learn for Edexcel's 9-1 International GCSE Biology exams... sometimes it can be hard to get motivated for a big revision session.

That's why we've made this fantastic little book — it's full of bite-sized tests, perfect for slotting into a convenient ten-minute slice of your life. And all the answers are included at the back, so it's easy to check your work. Very handy.

By the time you've reached the end, you'll have tested your knowledge of every IGCSE Biology topic* without even (well, hardly even) noticing...

* Every Biology topic from the Edexcel International GCSE Science Double Award is in here too.

CGP — still the best ☺

Our sole aim here at CGP is to produce the highest quality books — carefully written, immaculately presented and dangerously close to being funny.

Then we work our socks off to get them out to you — at the cheapest possible prices.

Published by CGP

Editors:
Charlotte Burrows, Jack Davies

ISBN: 978 1 78908 085 8

With thanks to Susan Alexander and Glenn Rogers for the proofreading.

Clipart from Corel®
Illustrations by: Sandy Gardner Artist, email sandy@sandygardner.co.uk
Printed by Elanders Ltd, Newcastle upon Tyne

Based on the classic CGP style created by Richard Parsons.

Contents

Paper 2

The questions in this book test both Biology Paper 1 and Biology Paper 2 material. Some material is needed for Paper 2 only — we've marked Paper 2 questions in Sections 1-9 with brackets like this one.

If you're doing a Science (Double Award) qualification you don't need to learn the Paper 2 material.

Test 1

There are **12 questions** in this test. Give yourself **10 minutes** to answer them all.

1. Which of these parts is **not** found in a bacterial cell?

A Nucleus

B Cell membrane

C Plasmids

[1]

2. Diffusion is the net movement of particles from...

A ... an area of lower concentration to an area of higher concentration.

B ... an area of higher concentration to an area of lower concentration.

[1]

3. Chloroplasts...

A ... strengthen a plant cell.

B ... store all the genetic material of a cell.

C ... absorb light energy to make glucose.

[1]

4. What are the cell walls of fungi made of?

A Cellulose

B Chitin

C Glycogen

[1]

5. Why is the shape of an enzyme important for its function?

A So that it can squeeze through small gaps.

B So that it can enter the cells of the body.

C So that it fits the substance involved in the reaction it is catalysing.

[1]

6. What is an organism that causes a disease called?

A An antibody

B An antigen

C A pathogen

[1]

7. Where in a cell do most of the reactions involved in aerobic respiration take place?

A The cytoplasm

B The nucleus

C The mitochondria

[1]

Paper 2

8. What is a cell called when it has differentiated?

A An unspecialised cell.

B A specialised cell.

C A stem cell.

[1]

9. Give one example of a virus.

Corona

[1]

10. Give two factors that affect the movement of substances into and out of cells.

1. Thickness of cell wall

2. Temperature

[2]

11. Give one advantage of using stem cells in medicine.

Paper 2

• Get healthy cells from one person and use the healthy cells to replace the faulty ones

[1]

12. Describe what happens to an enzyme if the temperature is too high.

The enzyme will denature meaning that it will change shape and will be unable to fit into the substance involved in the reaction.

[3]

15

Test 2

There are **11 questions** in this test. Give yourself **10 minutes** to answer them all.

1. What is the name for the process where perfume particles spread out in the air?

A Active transport

B Osmosis

C Diffusion

[1]

2. What is a vacuole?

A A large organelle in a plant cell which is filled with cell sap.

B A large organelle in a plant cell which contains chlorophyll.

[1]

3. Which of the following is a function of plant cell walls?

A To carry out protein synthesis.

B To control the cell's activities.

C To strengthen and support the cell.

[1]

4. Enzymes are biological catalysts that...

A ... slow down reactions in the body.

B ... speed up reactions in the body.

C ... are used up in reactions in the body.

[1]

5. True or False? "Pathogens include bacteria, protoctists and fungi only."

A True

B False

[1]

6. True or False? "In plant cells, the nucleus contains DNA."

A True

B False

[1]

7. A student investigates the effect of temperature on the reaction rate of amylase on the breakdown of starch to glucose. Which of the following is a variable that should be controlled in this experiment?

A Temperature

B pH

C Concentration of glucose

[1]

8. If you place a slice of potato in a solution that has a higher sugar concentration than the fluid inside the potato, the potato will...

A ... release water and decrease in mass.

B ... absorb water and increase in mass.

[1]

Paper 2

9. Give one disadvantage of using stem cells in medicine.

....

....
[1]

10. What is active transport?

....

....

....
[2]

11. Complete this diagram of an animal cell.

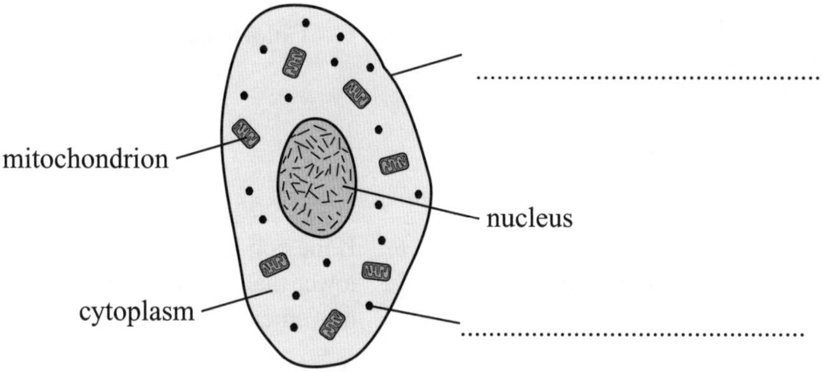

mitochondrion

nucleus

cytoplasm

....

....

Describe the roles of the following parts of a cell:

Mitochondria ....

....

Nucleus ....

....
[4]

15

Test 3

There are **12 questions** in this test. Give yourself **10 minutes** to answer them all.

1. Which process allows glucose to move from a higher concentration in the gut to a lower concentration in the blood?

A Active transport

B Osmosis

C Diffusion

[1]

2. An organism has a surface area of 20 m^2 and a volume of 8 m^3. What is its surface area to volume ratio in its simplest form?

A 2.5 : 1

B 4 : 1

C 1.5 : 1

[1]

3. What is a tissue?

A A group of different types of cell that work together to carry out a particular function.

B A collection of similar cells that work together to carry out a particular function.

[1]

4. Which of these organelles is found in plant cells but **not** in animal cells?

A Mitochondria

B Ribosomes

C Chloroplasts

[1]

5. Which of the following is **not** a basic characteristic shared by all living organisms?

A Respiration

B Reproduction

C Photosynthesis

[1]

6. If the concentration of water inside a cell is lower than outside the cell, what will the net movement of water molecules be?

A Into the cell

B Out of the cell

[1]

7. *Amoeba* is a type of...

A ... plant.

B ... protoctist.

C ... fungi.

[1]

Paper 2

8. What is a stem cell?

A A differentiated cell.

B An undifferentiated cell.

[1]

Paper 2

9. Explain what is meant by the term 'cell differentiation'.

....

....

[1]

10. What happens to the rate of diffusion across a cell membrane if the concentration gradient increases?

....

[1]

11. Explain why the function of an enzyme is reduced at very high pH.

....

....

....

....

[3]

12. What is a mycelium?

....

....

....

[2]

15

Test 4

There are **11 questions** in this test. Give yourself **10 minutes** to answer them all.

1. What colour is iodine solution in the presence of starch?

A Blue-black

B Browny-orange

C Brick-red

[1]

2. Proteases catalyse the breakdown of...

A ... lipids into glycerol.

B ... proteins into amino acids.

C ... carbohydrates into simple sugars.

[1]

3. What is a single lipid molecule made up of?

A Glycerol and fatty acids

B Amino acids

C Simple sugars

[1]

4. Which vitamin is needed to prevent scurvy?

A Vitamin A

B Vitamin C

C Vitamin D

[1]

5. Why is iron needed in the diet?

A To make bones and teeth.

B For calcium absorption.

C To make haemoglobin.

[1]

6. Where is bile produced and stored?

A Bile is produced in the liver and stored in the gall bladder.

B Bile is produced in the gall bladder and stored in the stomach.

C Bile is produced in the stomach and stored in the pancreas.

[1]

7. Children and teenagers generally need...

A ... more energy than older people.

B ... less energy than older people.

C ... the same amount of energy as older people.

[1]

8. Which substance is broken down by amylase?

A Starch

B Glycerol

C Protein

[1]

9. A food sample was burned and increased the temperature of 50 g of water by 16.6 °C. Use the following equation to calculate the amount of energy in the food sample in joules (J).

Energy in food (J) = Mass of water (g) × Temperature change of water (°C) × 4.2

....

.... J
[1]

10. Give three ways the small intestine is adapted for absorption of food.

1. ....

2. ....

3. ....
[3]

11. Complete this diagram of the human alimentary canal.

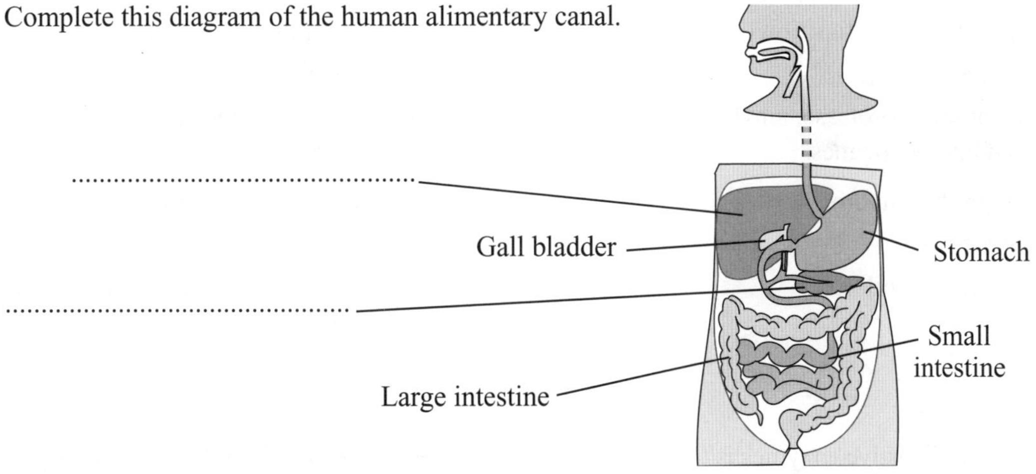

Describe the role of the large intestine.

....

....
[3]

15

Test 5

There are **12 questions** in this test. Give yourself **10 minutes** to answer them all.

1. Which of the following could you use to test for the presence of sugar in a food sample?

A Ethanol

B Benedict's solution

C Iodine solution

[1]

2. Which chemical elements are found in all proteins?

A Carbon, hydrogen, oxygen and iron.

B Carbon, hydrogen, oxygen and nitrogen.

C Carbon, potassium, oxygen and nitrogen.

[1]

3. Why is dietary fibre needed?

A To improve vision.

B To repair tissue.

C To aid the movement of food through the gut.

[1]

4. Pregnant women need...

A ... the same amount of energy as other women.

B ... more energy than other women.

C ... less energy than other women.

[1]

5. Which of these is a function of the pancreas?

A To produce protease, amylase and lipase enzymes.

B To produce hydrochloric acid and pepsin.

C To produce bile.

[1]

6. In the small intestine, why are villi covered in microvilli?

A To increase the surface area of the small intestine.

B To increase the blood supply of the small intestine.

C To increase the length of the small intestine.

[1]

7. The role of digestive enzymes is to...

A ... catalyse the breakdown of food into smaller, soluble molecules.

B ... catalyse the breakdown of food into smaller, insoluble molecules.

[1]

8. What is the Biuret test used to test for in a food sample?

A Starch

B Protein

C Lipids

[1]

Paper 2

9. A student investigated the energy content of a food sample by setting it on fire and holding it below a boiling tube of water being held by a clamp. She measured the change in the temperature of the water. Suggest an improvement to this method that could make her results more accurate.

....

....
[1]

10. Describe how peristalsis moves food through the gut.

....

....

....
[2]

11. Give two nutrients that a balanced diet should contain.

1. ....

2. ....
[2]

12. Explain how bile speeds up digestion by emulsifying fats.

....

....

....
[2]

15

Test 6

There are **12 questions** in this test. Give yourself **10 minutes** to answer them all.

1. Palisade mesophyll cells are adapted for photosynthesis. Which of these characteristics would help them to carry out this specialised function?

A Having a thick cell wall.

B Containing lots of chloroplasts.

C Being situated at the bottom of a leaf.

[1]

2. What would you expect to happen to the volume of oxygen produced by pondweed if light intensity increased, but temperature and carbon dioxide concentration stayed the same?

A It would increase.

B It would stay the same.

C It would decrease.

[1]

3. Which of these is most likely to affect the rate of photosynthesis?

A A change in wind speed.

B A change in oxygen concentration.

C A change in temperature.

[1]

4. Photosynthesis converts...

A ... chemical energy to light energy

B ... light energy to thermal energy

C ... light energy to chemical energy

[1]

5. True or False? "Xylem tubes transport dissolved sucrose around a plant."

A True

B False

[1]

6. What is the balanced chemical equation for photosynthesis?

A $CO_2 + H_2O \rightarrow C_6H_{12}O_6 + O_2$

B $3CO_2 + 3H_2O \rightarrow C_6H_{12}O_6 + 3O_2$

C $6CO_2 + 6H_2O \rightarrow C_6H_{12}O_6 + 6O_2$

[1]

7. Why do plants need magnesium?

A To make chlorophyll

B To make DNA

C To make proteins

[1]

Paper 2

8. Which word describes the evaporation of water from a plant's surface?

A Transpiration

B Photosynthesis

C Transcription

[1]

9. Explain why unicellular organisms can rely on diffusion to move substances in and out of a cell.

....

....

....

[2]

Paper 2

10. What type of plant cells absorb water from the soil?

....

[1]

11. Complete the word equation for photosynthesis.

.... energy

.... + water ⟶ .... + oxygen

[2]

12. Explain what happens to the rate of photosynthesis if a plant is put in a dark place.

....

....

....

[2]

15

Test 7

There are **11 questions** in this test. Give yourself **10 minutes** to answer them all.

1. What do phloem tubes transport?

A Oxygen

B Minerals

C Sucrose

[1]

2. True or False? "As the level of carbon dioxide increases, the rate of photosynthesis will always increase."

A True

B False

[1]

3. Other than oxygen, what does photosynthesis produce?

A Carbon dioxide

B Water

C Glucose

[1]

4. What is stored in glucose?

A Magnesium

B Chemical energy

C Nitrogen

[1]

5. Which of these mineral ions is needed to make amino acids?

A Nitrate

B Potassium

C Phosphate

[1]

6. If there is no starch in a leaf, this suggests that the leaf...

A ... has been able to photosynthesise.

B ... has not been able to photosynthesise.

[1]

7. Which of the following absorbs light in photosynthesis?

A Cytoplasm

B Chlorophyll

C Water

[1]

Paper 2

8. On which of the following days is a plant's water uptake likely to be the greatest?

A A sunny day

B A still day

C A cold day

[1]

9. Explain how the waxy cuticle on the surface of leaves aids efficient photosynthesis.

....

....

[1]

10. Name two factors that can affect the rate of photosynthesis.

1. ....

2. ....

[2]

Paper 2

11. Explain how increasing air movement around a plant's leaves would affect the rate of transpiration.

....

....

....

....

....

....

[4]

15

Test 8

There are **11 questions** in this test. Give yourself **10 minutes** to answer them all.

1. Which of these characteristics makes the alveoli efficient at gas exchange?

   A They have thick walls.

   B They have a large surface area.

   C They have poor blood supply.

   [1]

2. Which of these is produced by aerobic respiration but **not** by anaerobic respiration?

   A Water

   B Lactic acid

   C ATP

   [1]

3. When breathing in, which structure(s) does air enter first?

   A Alveoli

   B Trachea

   C Bronchi

   [1]

4. Which chemical formula represents a product of aerobic respiration?

   A $C_6H_{12}O_6$

   B O_2

   C CO_2

   [1]

5. Why does smoking increase the risk of coronary heart disease?

   A It increases blood pressure.

   B It makes blood clots less likely to form.

   C It reduces heart rate.

   [1]

6. Which of the following is a product of anaerobic respiration in animals?

   A Ethanol

   B Lactic acid

   C Hydrochloric acid

   [1]

7. What is the role of ATP?

   A It stores the energy needed for cell processes.

   B It provides the cell with oxygen.

   C It breaks down carbon dioxide in the cell.

   [1]

Paper 2

8. What substance, produced during photosynthesis, diffuses out of a plant via the stomata?

   A Glucose

   B Carbon dioxide

   C Oxygen

   [1]

9. Give two advantages of aerobic respiration over anaerobic respiration.

- Doesn't produce lactic acid - no cramps
- You will use more energy - Produces more ATP

[2]

10. In an experiment, it was found that carbon dioxide concentrations increased around leaves kept in the dark within a sealed container. Explain this result.

This shows that photosynthesis wasn't taking place due to being placed within the dark. As for photosynthesis to take place. CO_2 is one of the substances that is taken in and O_2 is the product

[3]

Paper 2

11. Explain how a hydrogen-carbonate indicator would show whether or not respiration was taking place in germinating seeds placed in a sealed test tube.

[2]

15

Test 9

There are **12 questions** in this test. Give yourself **10 minutes** to answer them all.

1. Why do alveoli have a moist lining?

A To reduce their surface area.

B To make their walls permeable.

C For gases to dissolve in.

[1]

2. Which type of respiration transfers more energy?

A Aerobic respiration

B Anaerobic respiration

[1]

3. Which of the following is produced by anaerobic respiration in plants?

A Lactic acid

B Ethanol

C Water

[1]

4. Pleural membranes surround...

A ... the heart.

B ... the trachea.

C ... the lungs.

[1]

5. Energy transferred by respiration is used to make molecules of what?

A Glucose

B Oxygen

C ATP

[1]

6. True or False? "Anaerobic respiration requires oxygen."

A True

B False

[1]

7. Doing vigorous exercise causes your...

A ... respiration rate to decrease.

B ... breathing rate to increase.

C ... heart rate to decrease.

[1]

8. When a plant is under high light intensity...

Paper 2

A ... it releases more oxygen than it takes in.

B ... it releases less oxygen than it takes in.

[1]

9. Give one problem caused by tar from cigarettes.

....

....

[1]

10. Complete this diagram of the human thorax.

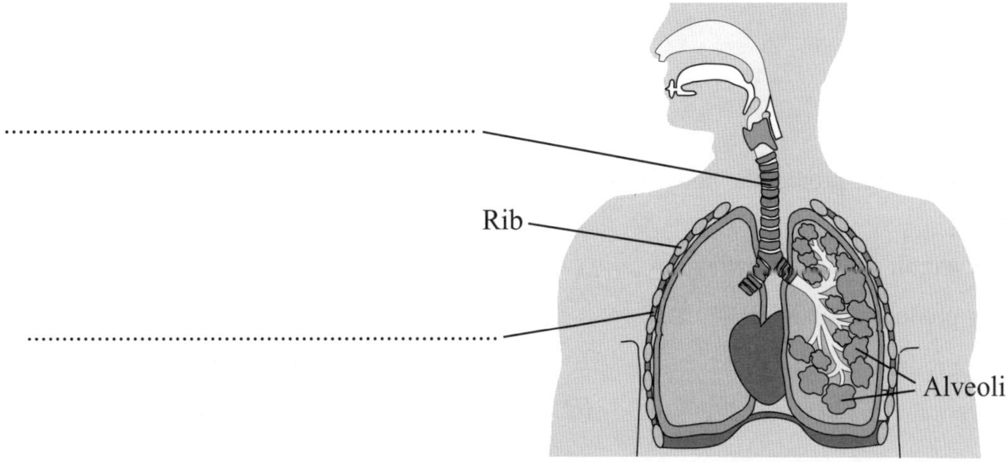

....

Rib

....

Alveoli

[2]

11. Explain the role of the intercostal muscles and the diaphragm in breathing out.

....

....

[2]

12. Explain why a leaf's stomata close during the night.

Paper 2

....

....

[2]

15

Test 10

There are **12 questions** in this test. Give yourself **10 minutes** to answer them all.

1. What do lymphocytes produce to help defend against pathogens?

A Antigens

B Antibiotics

C Antibodies

[1]

2. Which of these are **not** features of arteries?

A Elastic fibres

B Thick walls

C Valves

[1]

3. How do phagocytes protect the body from pathogens?

A They engulf and ingest pathogens.

B They produce antibodies.

C They produce lymphocytes.

[1]

4. Which of these blood vessels carries blood to the kidneys?

A Hepatic artery

B Renal artery

C Pulmonary artery

[1]

5. Which of these is **not** a chamber of the heart?

A Left ventricle

B Right atrium

C Vena cava

[1]

6. Which of the following is **not** a way that red blood cells are specialised for their function?

A They have a biconcave disc shape to give a large surface area.

B They don't have a nucleus to allow more room to carry oxygen.

C They contain lots of mitochondria so that they have energy to move around the body.

[1]

7. Capillaries are able to exchange substances with cells in the body because...

A ... they have valves.

B ... they have permeable walls.

C ... they have a large lumen.

[1]

Paper 2

8. Which of the following substances are reabsorbed by the kidneys?

A Glucose and water.

B Water and urea.

C ADH and glucose.

[1]

9. Give one risk factor for coronary heart disease.

Smoking

[1]

10. Give one effect that adrenaline has on the heart.

Increases your heart rate

[1]

11. Give two differences between arteries and veins.

1. The arteries carry blood away from the heart whereas veins carry towards

2. Arteries are large and have thick walls whereas a veins wall is permeable

[2]

12. Explain how vaccination can protect against a disease.

Paper 2

The vaccination gives the body a small amount of a disease and the body produces antibodies that are there for a long time and make you immuen

[3]

15

Test 11

There are **11 questions** in this test. Give yourself **10 minutes** to answer them all.

1. What is the function of white blood cells?

- **A** They deliver nutrients around the body.
- **B** They transport deoxygenated blood around the body.
- **C** They defend the body against microorganisms.

[1]

2. Which of these is **not** a component of blood?

- **A** Platelets
- **B** Lumen
- **C** Plasma

[1]

3. Alex walked to catch the bus, but Peter was late so had to run. Whose heart rate will be higher?

- **A** Alex
- **B** Peter

[1]

4. True or False? "Blood flows to the organs through veins."

- **A** True
- **B** False

[1]

5. The hepatic vein carries blood away from which organ?

- **A** Liver
- **B** Heart
- **C** Gut

[1]

6. Which of these is **not** an excretory product of the kidneys?

- **A** Ions
- **B** Urea
- **C** Amino acids

[1]

7. The presence of haemoglobin in red blood cells is an adaptation for...

- **A** ... reducing blood pressure.
- **B** ... storing iron.
- **C** ... carrying oxygen.

[1]

Paper 2

8. True or False? "Vaccinations usually involve injecting small amounts of dead or inactive pathogens into the body."

- **A** True
- **B** False

[1]

9. Explain why the left ventricle of the heart has a thicker wall than the right ventricle.

It needs to be thicker as its pumping blood around the entire body and not just lungs so needs to be stronger

[2]

10. Give three things transported in the blood plasma.

1. ....

2. ....

3. ....

[3]

11. Complete this diagram of the urinary system.

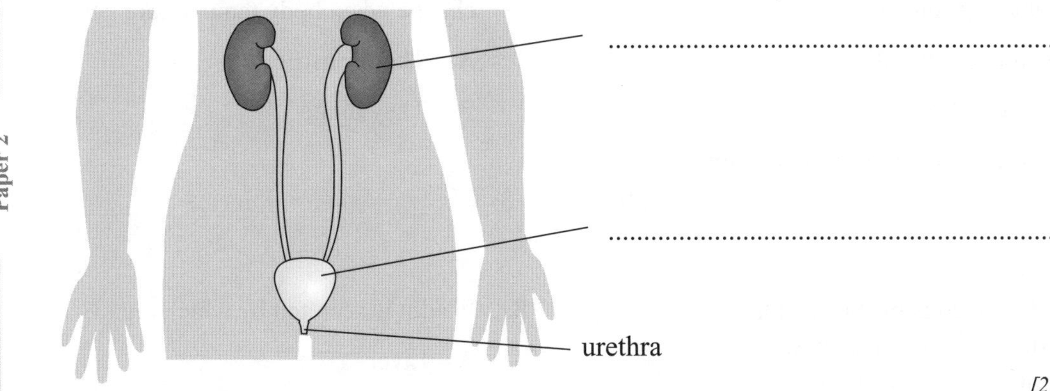

[2]

Paper 2

15

Test 12

There are **12 questions** in this test. Give yourself **10 minutes** to answer them all.

1. What is the function of the iris?

A To detect light.

B To focus light onto the retina.

C To control how much light enters the pupil.

[1]

2. What is the central nervous system made up of?

A The brain and receptors

B The brain and the spinal cord

C The spinal cord and receptors

[1]

3. Which is the correct pathway for stimuli along a reflex arc?

A relay neurone → sensory neurone → motor neurone

B sensory neurone → motor neurone → relay neurone

C sensory neurone → relay neurone → motor neurone

[1]

4. Which hormone controls the 'fight or flight' response?

A Adrenaline

B Insulin

C Oestrogen

[1]

5. What is the role of effectors in producing a coordinated response?

A To produce stimuli.

B To detect stimuli.

C To bring about a response to stimuli.

[1]

6. How do blood vessels supplying the skin change when body temperature gets too low?

A They constrict

B They dilate

[1]

7. A sprouting seed is planted so that the shoot is pointing sideways. Which side will grow faster?

A The lower side

B The upper side

[1]

8. Insulin is secreted by which organ?

A Liver

B Pancreas

C Adrenal glands

[1]

9. Describe how electrical impulses are transferred from neurone to neurone.

....

....

....

[2]

10. What is the role of progesterone in the menstrual cycle?

....

[1]

11. What is meant by the term 'homeostasis'?

....

....

[1]

12. Describe the changes that happen in the eye to allow it to focus on distant objects.

....

....

....

....

[3]

15

Test 13

There are **12 questions** in this test. Give yourself **10 minutes** to answer them all.

1. On which side of a plant shoot will more auxin accumulate when the shoot is exposed to light?

A The side in the light.

B The shaded side.

C Equally on the light and shaded sides.

[1]

2. In order to cool the body down, sweat glands...

A ... produce less sweat.

B ... produce more sweat.

C ... absorb sweat.

[1]

3. Which of the following hormones causes the liver to turn glucose into glycogen?

A Testosterone

B Adrenaline

C Insulin

[1]

4. True or False? "Hormones have longer-lasting effects than nervous impulses."

A True

B False

[1]

5. Within the eye, the lens is responsible for...

A ... controlling the diameter of the pupil.

B ... carrying impulses to the brain.

C ... focusing light onto the retina.

[1]

6. A change in the internal or external environment is called...

A ... a stimulus.

B ... an effector.

C ... an impulse.

[1]

7. A reflex arc...

A ... only involves the brain.

B ... only involves the conscious part of the brain.

C ... doesn't involve the conscious part of the brain.

[1]

Paper 2

8. Which of the following hormones is produced in the ovaries?

A Oestrogen

B FSH

C Adrenaline

[1]

9. What links the central nervous system to the sense organs?

....

[1]

10. What is the function of a receptor in coordinating a response?

....

[1]

11. List two internal conditions that your body needs to keep constant to survive.

1. ....

2. ....

[2]

12. Explain how blood vessels help to reduce core body temperature when it gets too high.

....

....

....

....

....

[3]

15

Test 14

There are **12 questions** in this test. Give yourself **10 minutes** to answer them all.

1. What happens at the start of mitosis?

A The cytoplasm divides.

B The arms of the chromosomes are pulled to opposite ends of the cell.

C The chromosomes are duplicated.

[1]

2. What is an organism's genotype?

A The characteristics that the organism has.

B The alleles that the organism has.

[1]

3. Which of the following describes an organism that has two different alleles for a trait?

A Homozygous

B Heterozygous

C Haploid

[1]

4. In what type of reproduction do gametes fuse together?

A Asexual

B Sexual

[1]

5. During pregnancy, what chance is there of a woman having a baby boy?

A 50%

B 25%

C 75%

[1]

6. True or False? "It's completely random which organisms survive and pass on their genes to the next generation."

A True

B False

[1]

Paper 2

7. Which of the following statements is true about base pairing in DNA?

A A always pairs with T and C always pairs with G.

B A always pairs with C and G always pairs with T.

C A always pairs with G and T always pairs with C.

[1]

Paper 2

8. How often do mutations have a significant effect on phenotype?

A Always

B Often

C Very rarely

[1]

9. Where does a germinating seed get its energy from, before it has green leaves?

....
[1]

10. Describe the role of the pollen tube during fertilisation in plants.

....

....

....
[2]

11. Give the function of these parts of the male reproductive system:

Erectile tissue ....

....

Vas deferens ....

....
[2]

12. Give two uses of mitosis in multicellular organisms.

1. ....

2. ....
[2]

15

Test 15

There are **11 questions** in this test. Give yourself **10 minutes** to answer them all.

1. If a cell is diploid, how many copies of each chromosome does it have?

A One

B Two

C Four

[1]

2. If a dog with long hair (Hh) was bred with a dog with short hair (hh), what possible combinations of alleles could be produced?

A hh

B HH

C Hh, hh

[1]

3. When an individual has one dominant and one recessive allele...

A ... the recessive allele is expressed.

B ... both alleles are expressed.

C ... the dominant allele is expressed.

[1]

4. How many chromosomes does a human haploid cell have?

A 46

B 92

C 23

[1]

5. What sex chromosomes does someone who is biologically male have?

A XY

B XXX

C XX

[1]

6. True or False? "Mitosis results in two cells that are genetically different."

A True

B False

[1]

Paper 2

7. Ionising radiation and chemical mutagens...

A ... increase the chance of mutation.

B ... reduce the chance of mutation.

C ... have no effect on the chance of mutation.

[1]

Paper 2

8. The translation stage of protein synthesis takes place on which of the following organelles?

A Ribosomes

B Mitochondria

C Chloroplasts

[1]

9. How does fertilisation produce genetic variation?

....

....
[1]

10. Give two ways that flowers can be adapted to attract insects for pollination.

1. ....

2. ....
[2]

11. Explain how resistance to an antibiotic could increase within a bacterial population.

....

....

....

....

....

....
[4]

15

Test 16

There are **11 questions** in this test. Give yourself **10 minutes** to answer them all.

1. What is the main idea behind Darwin's theory of evolution by natural selection?

A There is variation in a population. Those more suited to the environment will be more likely to survive and pass on their characteristics.

B Individuals develop characteristics during their lifetimes which make them more suited to their environment. They pass these on to their offspring.

[1]

2. Variation within a species is caused by...

A ... genetic factors only.

B ... environmental factors only.

C ... a mixture of genetic and environmental factors.

[1]

3. True or False? "Some gametes are genetically identical to each other."

A True

B False

[1]

4. Most characteristics are controlled by...

A ... a single gene.

B ... several genes interacting.

[1]

5. What is a gene?

A An amino acid

B A protein

C A section of DNA

[1]

6. Which hormone promotes the development of female secondary sexual characteristics?

A Progesterone

B Testosterone

C Oestrogen

[1]

7. Which one of these statements is true about genetic mutations?

A Mutations can be inherited.

B Mutations happen very often in a gene.

C Mutations are non-random.

[1]

Paper 2

8. What structure does DNA have?

A A long, single, straight chain

B A triple helix structure

C A double helix structure

[1]

9. What is the function of the amniotic fluid during pregnancy?

....

....
[1]

10. Describe one natural method of asexual reproduction used by a plant.

....

....

....
[2]

11. Cystic fibrosis is a genetic disorder caused by a recessive allele. Rachael and Henry are about to have a child. Both of them carry the cystic fibrosis allele, but do not have the disease. Complete the genetic diagram to show the possible genotypes of the child.

Use **F** to represent the dominant allele and **f** to represent the recessive allele.

Ff Ff

What is the chance that their child will have cystic fibrosis?
Explain your answer.

....

....

....

....
[4]

15

Test 17

There are **11 questions** in this test. Give yourself **10 minutes** to answer them all.

1. Which type of cell division produces gametes?

A Meiosis

B Mitosis

[1]

2. True or False? "The genome is the entire DNA of an organism."

A True

B False

[1]

3. What is a fertilised egg cell also known as?

A A zygote

B A gamete

C A daughter cell

[1]

4. What are alleles?

A Male sex chromosomes

B Two gametes fused together

C Different versions of the same gene

[1]

5. What is one role of oestrogen in the menstrual cycle?

A To inhibit the release of LH.

B To cause the lining of the uterus to grow.

C To cause an egg to mature in one of the ovaries.

[1]

6. Which of the following allows the exchange of food, oxygen and waste between the blood of the mother and the blood of the embryo?

A Amniotic fluid

B Wall of the uterus

C Placenta

[1]

Paper 2

7. The order of amino acids in a protein is determined by...

A ... the order of bases in the gene.

B ... the shape of the protein.

C ... the order of genes in the DNA.

[1]

Paper 2

8. What four bases does DNA contain?

A A, B, C and D

B A, C, G and T

C A, C, E and G

[1]

9. In an experiment, seeds were found to germinate when placed in a boiling tube of water. Seeds did not germinate when placed in a boiling tube of water with a layer of oil. Explain why.

....

....

[1]

10. A tall pea plant with two dominant 'T' alleles and a dwarf pea plant with two recessive 't' alleles are crossed to produce a pea plant with the genotype Tt. What will the new plant's phenotype be? Explain your answer.

....

....

....

[2]

11. Describe the process of evolution by natural selection.

....

....

....

....

....

....

....

[4]

15

Test 18

There are **12 questions** in this test. Give yourself **10 minutes** to answer them all.

1. An organism's habitat refers to...

A ... the other organisms living in the surrounding area.

B ... the place where it lives.

C ... the non-living conditions in the surrounding area.

[1]

2. Which of these human activities is most likely to increase the amount of nitrous oxide released into the atmosphere?

A Growing rice.

B Using aerosol sprays.

C Using fertiliser on soils.

[1]

3. In a pyramid of energy transfer, the only energy that can be transferred to the next trophic level is...

A ... the energy transferred by heat.

B ... the energy in indigestible food.

C ... the energy that becomes biomass.

[1]

4. What is meant by 'a population'?

A All the organisms of different species in a habitat.

B All the organisms of one species in a habitat.

C A community of organisms and all the abiotic conditions of their habitat.

[1]

5. Which of the following is an abiotic factor?

A Temperature

B Predation

C Competition

[1]

6. Greenhouse gases...

A ... increase the amount of energy kept in the atmosphere.

B ... decrease the amount of energy kept in the atmosphere.

[1]

7. Which of these gases can cause acid rain?

A Sulfur dioxide

B Carbon dioxide

C Carbon monoxide

[1]

Paper 2

8. What role do nitrogen-fixing bacteria play in the nitrogen cycle?

A They turn ammonia into nitrites and then nitrates.

B They turn nitrates into nitrogen gas.

C They turn atmospheric nitrogen into ammonia.

[1]

9. How does respiration contribute to the carbon cycle?

....
[1]

10. Why is carbon monoxide poisonous to humans?

....

....

....
[2]

11. Give two ways that energy can be lost from a food chain.

1. ....

2. ....
[2]

12. A biologist used a quadrat with an area of 0.25 m^2 to randomly sample limpets on a beach. The mean number of limpets per quadrat was 22. The area of the beach was 1800 m^2. Estimate the population of limpets on the beach.

....

....

.... limpets
[2]

15

Test 19

There are **11 questions** in this test. Give yourself **10 minutes** to answer them all.

1. True or false? "Communities are affected by both abiotic and biotic factors."

A True

B False

[1]

2. Food chains always start with which trophic level?

A Primary consumers

B Producers

C Decomposers

[1]

3. If a new predator arrives in an area, will the size of the prey population increase or decrease?

A Increase

B Decrease

[1]

4. All the organisms of different species living in a habitat are know as...

A ... a population.

B ... a genus.

C ... a community.

[1]

5. Which of these would be represented by the smallest bar on a pyramid of biomass?

A Grass

B Rabbit

C Fox

[1]

6. True or False? "None of the Sun's energy is lost throughout a food chain."

A True

B False

[1]

7. Which of the following processes removes carbon dioxide from the air?

A Respiration

B Decomposition

C Photosynthesis

[1]

Paper 2

8. Nitrifying bacteria turn ammonium ions...

A ... into nitrogen gas.

B ... into nitrates.

C ... into urea.

[1]

Paper 2

9. What is biodiversity?

....

....

[1]

10. Give two human activities that are increasing the amount of carbon dioxide in the atmosphere.

1. ....

2. ....

[2]

11. Explain how excess nitrates from fertilisers can cause eutrophication if they get into rivers and lakes.

....

....

....

....

....

....

[4]

15

Test 20

There are **12 questions** in this test. Give yourself **10 minutes** to answer them all.

1. Which of these stages in the carbon cycle does **not** release carbon dioxide into the air?

   A Combustion

   B Respiration

   C Photosynthesis

   [1]

2. A producer...

   A ... is eaten by secondary consumers.

   B ... makes glucose from photosynthesis.

   C ... is also a primary consumer.

   [1]

3. Roughly, what percentage of the biomass from a trophic level is transferred to the trophic level above?

   A 0%

   B 10%

   C 50%

   [1]

4. True or False? "A pyramid of biomass shows the number of organisms at each stage of a food chain."

   A True

   B False

   [1]

5. Which of the following is **not** a greenhouse gas?

   A Methane

   B Water vapour

   C Oxygen

   [1]

6. Competition is an example of...

   A ... a biotic factor.

   B ... an abiotic factor.

   [1]

7. Which of these problems can be caused by the pollution of water with sewage?

   A Soil erosion

   B Acid rain

   C Eutrophication

   [1]

8. What is a quadrat?

   A A line through a habitat along which distribution is studied.

   B A square frame enclosing a known area.

   C A piece of apparatus that measures water uptake in plants.

   [1]

9. How does the amount of biomass change along a food chain?

....

....
[1]

10. Suggest one biotic factor that might cause a decrease in the population of a species.

....
[1]

11. A large number of thrushes in a woodland have died. Use the food web to suggest the effect this could have on the number of hawks and snails.

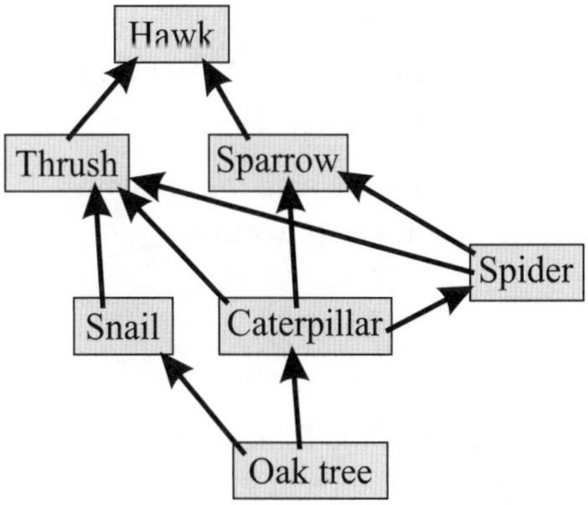

Hawks ....

....

Snails ....

....
[2]

12. Explain how the increase in the amount of greenhouse gases in the atmosphere is causing global warming.

....

....

....

....
[3]

__ / **15**

Test 21

There are **11 questions** in this test. Give yourself **10 minutes** to answer them all.

1. Which enzyme cuts DNA at specific sites?

A A restriction enzyme

B Maltase

C Ligase

[1]

2. True or False? "Increasing the carbon dioxide concentration in a glasshouse could increase the crop yield."

A True

B False

[1]

3. What is the main reason why the temperature needs to be controlled in a fermenter?

A To keep out unwanted microbes.

B To make sure the pH is at the optimum level.

C To make sure the enzymes don't stop working.

[1]

4. Which of the following is a disadvantage of using biological control as a method of pest control?

A It can lead to eutrophication.

B It can be more harmful to wildlife than chemical pesticides.

C The organisms used can become pests themselves.

[1]

5. Which of the following is true about growing crops in glasshouses?

A It's harder to keep crops free of pests and diseases.

B The temperature is cooler inside glasshouses than it is outside.

C Artificial light can be used at night to give crops more time to photosynthesise.

[1]

6. Biological control means...

A ... controlling pests using chemicals.

B ... controlling pests using other organisms.

C ... controlling pests by capturing them in traps.

[1]

7. True or False? "Selective breeding can happen without human intervention."

A True

B False

[1]

8. Fertilisers help increase crop yield by...

A ... killing crop pests.

B ... adding minerals to the soil.

C ... increasing the amount of nutrients that are leached away.

[1]

9. What is meant by the term 'transgenic'?

....

.... [1]

10. A student wants to test the effect of changing temperature on anaerobic respiration in yeast using the equipment shown in the diagram. Suggest a way he could measure respiration rate.

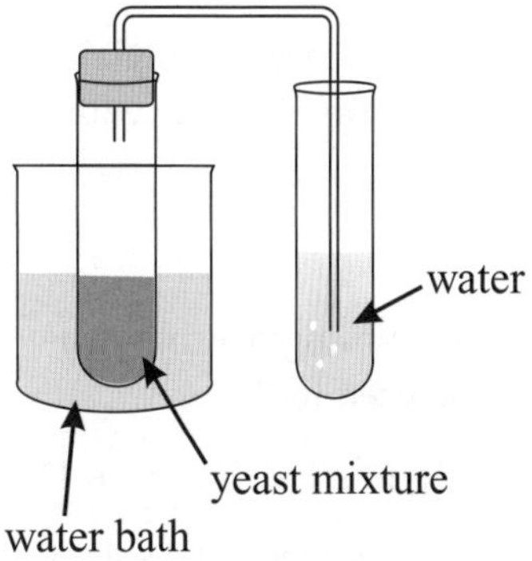

....

....

....

.... [2]

Paper 2

11. Describe how micropropagation is used to produce cloned plants.

....

....

....

....

....

.... [4]

15

Test 22

There are **11 questions** in this test. Give yourself **10 minutes** to answer them all.

1. In glasshouses, an increased temperature...

A ... decreases crop yield, by decreasing the rate of photosynthesis.

B ... increases crop yield, by increasing the rate of photosynthesis.

C ... increases crop yield, by decreasing the rate of photosynthesis.

[1]

2. If a farmer wants to increase the meat yield of his cattle, he would breed from...

A ... the biggest cows.

B ... the cows that produce the most milk.

C ... those with a gentle temperament.

[1]

3. In genetic engineering, what is the enzyme ligase used for?

A To join two pieces of DNA together.

B To cut DNA at a specific sequence.

C To break down the DNA.

[1]

4. Yeast helps bread dough to rise by...

A ... producing sugars.

B ... producing alcohol.

C ... producing carbon dioxide.

[1]

5. What is the advantage of genetically modifying crop plants to make them resistant to herbicides?

A Crop yield is decreased.

B The crops are resistant to insects.

C Crop yield is increased.

[1]

6. Which microorganism is used in the production of yoghurt?

A *Pneumococcus*

B *Chlorella*

C *Lactobacillus*

[1]

7. True or False? "Insulin can be produced by bacteria that contain the human gene for insulin."

A True

B False

[1]

Paper 2

8. Which of these statements about farming fish in cages is true?

A The fish are less prone to disease.

B Interspecific predation is reduced.

C The fish use more energy to swim about.

[1]

9. Why are pesticides sprayed on crops?

....
[1]

10. What is the role of a vector in genetic engineering?

....

....

Give one example of a vector used in genetic engineering.

....
[3]

11. Explain how selective breeding could be used to increase the height of sunflowers.

....

....

....

....

....
[3]

15

Test 23

There are **12 questions** in this test. Give yourself **10 minutes** to answer them all.

1. True or False? "Synapses connect receptors."

A True

B False

[1]

2. The active transport of minerals means that they are absorbed into a cell...

A ... against the concentration gradient.

B ... down the concentration gradient.

[1]

3. Is a person who has two X chromosomes biologically male or female?

A Male

B Female

[1]

4. Which of the following substances do animals need to take in from the environment?

A Urea

B Oxygen

C Carbon dioxide

[1]

5. True or False? "Increasing the temperature always causes the rate of photosynthesis to increase."

A True

B False

[1]

6. An ecosystem is...

A ... the individuals of a species that live in a habitat.

B ... a community of living organisms.

C ... a community of living organisms and the non-living conditions of their environment.

[1]

7. Vasodilation of blood vessels close to the surface of the skin occurs when...

A ... you're too cold.

B ... you're too hot.

C ... you have a high blood glucose level.

[1]

8. Why do alveoli need a good blood supply?

A To maintain the concentration gradients of oxygen and carbon dioxide.

B To increase their surface area.

C To minimise the distances the gases have to move.

[1]

9. What is the function of valves in the heart?

....
[1]

10. Name the artery that joins the right ventricle of the heart to the lungs.

....
[1]

11. What is osmosis?

....

....

....
[2]

12. Explain why multicellular organisms need transport systems.

....

....

....

....

....
[3]

___
15

Test 24

There are **11 questions** in this test. Give yourself **10 minutes** to answer them all.

1. True or False? "Some bacteria can photosynthesise."

A True

B False

[1]

2. The left atrium receives blood from...

A ... the lungs.

B ... the brain.

C ... the muscles.

[1]

3. What carries hormones from where they're produced to other parts of the body?

A Nerves

B Plasma

C Platelets

[1]

4. True or False? "Respiration provides the energy needed for cell processes."

A True

B False

[1]

5. Which of the following hormones is produced in the testes?

A Oestrogen

B Progesterone

C Testosterone

[1]

6. Which level of organisation in organisms comes between cells and organs?

A Organ systems

B Organelles

C Tissues

[1]

7. What is the correct equation for anaerobic respiration in muscles?

A glucose + oxygen → carbon dioxide + water

B glucose → lactic acid

C glucose → carbon dioxide

[1]

8. In a plant shoot, does auxin increase or inhibit growth?

A Increase

B Inhibit

[1]

9. Give two mineral ions that plants need to take in from the environment.

1. ....

2. ....

[2]

10. What is the function of xylem vessels?

....

....

[1]

11. Explain how heart rate increases during exercise.

....

....

....

....

....

....

[4]

15

Test 25

There are **12 questions** in this test. Give yourself **10 minutes** to answer them all.

1. True or False? "Organ systems work together to form organs."

A True

B False

[1]

2. When breathing in, the diaphragm...

A ... contracts.

B ... relaxes.

[1]

3. Which of these is **not** part of the small intestine?

A Ileum

B Duodenum

C Colon

[1]

4. Which of these is excreted by the skin?

A Carbon dioxide

B Sweat

C Urea

[1]

5. True or False? "In a pyramid of numbers, each bar is always longer than the bar immediately below it."

A True

B False

[1]

6. What are plant cell walls made from?

A Glycogen

B Chitin

C Cellulose

[1]

7. What happens during fertilisation?

A A male and female gamete fuse together.

B The zygote undergoes cell division.

C Haploid gametes are produced.

[1]

8. Which part of animal and plant cells contains the chromosomes?

A Cytoplasm

B Cell membrane

C Nucleus

[1]

9. Give two ways that the structure of plant leaves is adapted for photosynthesis.

1. ....

2. ....

[2]

10. In what form is information transmitted from receptors in sense organs to the central nervous system?

....

[1]

11. Give two similarities in structure between animal and plant cells.

1. ....

2. ....

[2]

12. Explain how increasing carbon dioxide concentration in glasshouses can increase crop yield.

....

....

....

[2]

15

Test 26

There are **12 questions** in this test. Give yourself **10 minutes** to answer them all.

1. When organisms die they are broken down by...

A ... producers.

B ... secondary consumers.

C ... decomposers.

[1]

2. A rare, random change in an organism's DNA that can be inherited is called...

A ... a gene.

B ... a mutation.

C ... a mutagen.

[1]

3. True or False? "An organ is a group of similar cells that work together to carry out a particular function."

A True

B False

[1]

4. In what form do animals store carbohydrates?

A As glycogen

B As sucrose

C As starch

[1]

5. Why are aseptic conditions important when growing microorganisms in fermenters?

A To make sure the microorganisms have enough oxygen.

B To keep the temperature at the optimum level.

C To make sure the microorganisms aren't competing with other organisms.

[1]

6. True or False? "Viruses are living organisms."

A True

B False

[1]

7. Which of the following hormones increases heart rate?

A Oestrogen

B Insulin

C Adrenaline

[1]

8. Which of the following substances neutralises stomach acid?

A Bile

B Blood

C Pepsin

[1]

9. Give one stimulus that a plant might respond to.

....

[1]

10. Give the function of these parts of the female reproductive system:

Fallopian tube ....

....

Endometrium ....

....

[2]

11. Give two differences between nervous and hormonal responses.

1. ....

2. ....

[2]

12. Give two ways that the flowers of wind-pollinated plants are adapted for wind pollination.

1. ....

2. ....

[2]

15

Test 27

There are **12 questions** in this test. Give yourself **10 minutes** to answer them all.

1. Glycogen is made up of...

A ... amino acids.

B ... simple sugars.

C ... fatty acids and glycerol.

[1]

2. Which part of the blood is responsible for blood clotting?

A Red blood cells

B White blood cells

C Platelets

[1]

3. How is a decrease in temperature likely to affect the rate of transpiration from leaves?

A It will increase the rate of transpiration.

B It will decrease the rate of transpiration.

C It will have no overall effect on the rate of transpiration.

[1]

4. What role do denitrifying bacteria play in the nitrogen cycle?

A They turn nitrates into nitrogen gas.

B They turn ammonium ions into nitrates.

C They turn atmospheric nitrogen into ammonia.

[1]

5. What effect does ADH have on the collecting ducts of nephrons?

A It causes less water to be reabsorbed from them.

B It causes ions to be reabsorbed from them.

C It causes more water to be reabsorbed from them.

[1]

6. Which of the following describes the role of LH in the menstrual cycle?

A To cause an egg to mature in an ovary.

B To stimulate the release of an egg from an ovary.

C To maintain the lining of the uterus.

[1]

7. When trees are cut down...

A ... evapotranspiration is reduced and the local climate may become drier.

B ... evapotranspiration is increased and the local climate may become wetter.

[1]

8. A plant cutting lost 0.15 cm^3 of water in 20 minutes. What was its transpiration rate?

A 7.5×10^{-3} cm^3 min^{-1}

B 0.13 cm^3 min^{-1}

C 1.21×10^{-2} cm^3 min^{-1}

[1]

9. Name the part of the nephron where all the glucose is reabsorbed from.

....

[1]

10. Describe the process of saprotrophic nutrition used by fungi.

....

....

....

[2]

11. Describe how the following changes affect the rate of diffusion across an exchange surface:

A greater concentration gradient ....

A greater distance ....

[2]

12. Name the blood vessel that carries blood from the lungs to the heart.

....

Name the blood vessel that carries blood from the heart to the body.

....

[2]

15

Test 28

There are **12 questions** in this test. Give yourself **10 minutes** to answer them all.

1. How does carbon dioxide move into a leaf?

A By diffusion.

B By osmosis.

C By active transport.

[1]

2. True or False? "All consumers eat producers."

A True

B False

[1]

3. The hormone FSH has which of the following effects?

A Maintains the lining of the uterus.

B Stimulates the release of an egg from an ovary.

C Causes an egg to mature in an ovary.

[1]

4. Urine normally contains...

A ... water, urea and glucose.

B ... water, urea and ions.

C ... water and urea only.

[1]

5. True or False? "Cloned transgenic animals can be used to produce human proteins."

A True

B False

[1]

6. How many bases are needed to code for one amino acid?

A One

B Three

C Four

[1]

7. Having codominant alleles means that...

A ... characteristics from both alleles are shown.

B ... characteristics from only one allele are shown.

[1]

8. Which of the following describes the flow of liquid through a nephron?

A Bowman's capsule → glomerulus → collecting duct → loop of Henle

B glomerulus → Bowman's capsule → loop of Henle → collecting duct

C collecting duct → Bowman's capsule → glomerulus → loop of Henle

[1]

9. Explain why the glomerular filtrate does not contain proteins or blood cells.

....

....

....
[2]

10. Once the brain has detected that the water content of the blood is too low, describe how the water content is returned to a normal level.

....

....
[2]

11. Cystic fibrosis is a genetic disease caused by a recessive allele, 'f'. The dominant allele is 'F'. On the right is a family pedigree for a family that includes carriers of cystic fibrosis, with family members labelled A-F.

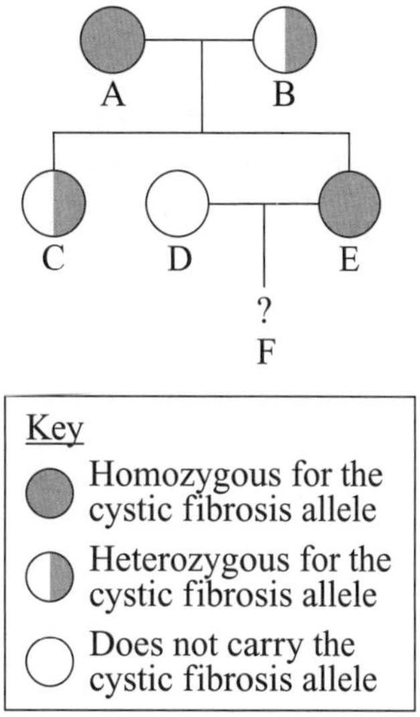

A B C D E ? F

Key
Homozygous for the cystic fibrosis allele
Heterozygous for the cystic fibrosis allele
Does not carry the cystic fibrosis allele

What genotype does person A have?

....

What is the probability that person F will be heterozygous for the cystic fibrosis allele?

....
[2]

12. What apparatus can be used to estimate transpiration rate?

....
[1]

___ / 15

Test 29

There are **11 questions** in this test. Give yourself **10 minutes** to answer them all.

1. What colour would a hydrogen-carbonate indicator turn if the CO_2 concentration in the air decreases?

A Purple

B Yellow

C Orange

[1]

2. Where is the hormone LH produced?

A Ovaries

B Pancreas

C Pituitary gland

[1]

3. An RNA molecule is...

A ... single stranded.

B ... double stranded.

C ... triple stranded.

[1]

4. Balancing the water coming into the body against the water going out is called...

A ... ultrafiltration.

B ... excretion.

C ... osmoregulation.

[1]

5. Which type of bacteria breaks down proteins and urea into ammonia in the nitrogen cycle?

A Nitrifying bacteria

B Decomposers

C Denitrifying bacteria

[1]

6. Which of these processes is called peristalsis?

A Muscle action that moves food through the gut.

B Maintaining a constant internal environment.

C The movement of particles against a concentration gradient.

[1]

7. Plant shoots are...

A ... positively phototropic and positively geotropic.

B ... negatively phototropic and positively geotropic.

C ... positively phototropic and negatively geotropic.

[1]

8. What part of the nephron connects the proximal convoluted tubule and the distal convoluted tubule?

A Collecting duct

B Loop of Henle

C Bowman's capsule

[1]

9. Give one reason why the diet of farmed fish is carefully controlled.

....

....

[1]

10. Explain why the transpiration rate of a plant is lower when the air around the plant is more humid.

....

....

....

[2]

11. How does cutting down and burning trees affect the balance of carbon dioxide and oxygen in the atmosphere?

....

....

....

....

....

....

[4]

15

Test 30

There are **11 questions** in this test. Give yourself **10 minutes** to answer them all.

1. True or False? "Water is reabsorbed from collecting ducts in the kidneys by active transport."

A True

B False

[1]

2. Which of these hormones is **not** produced by the pituitary gland?

A Adrenaline

B FSH

C ADH

[1]

3. True or False? "Micropropagation produces plants that are genetically different to each other."

A True

B False

[1]

4. Which base is **not** present in RNA?

A Cytosine

B Guanine

C Thymine

[1]

5. What connects each kidney to the bladder?

A Ureter

B Urethra

C Nephron

[1]

6. Which hormone triggers the development of secondary sexual characteristics in males?

A Progesterone

B LH

C Testosterone

[1]

7. Ultrafiltration happens between...

A ... the renal artery and the glomerulus.

B ... the glomerulus and the Bowman's capsule.

C ... the Bowman's capsule and the proximal convoluted tubule.

[1]

8. What is germination?

A When gametes fuse together.

B When photosynthesis first begins.

C When seeds start to grow.

[1]

9. A student investigates the effect of pH on the reaction rate of amylase on starch solution. Give one example of a variable that must be controlled in this investigation.

....

How could this variable be controlled?

....

[2]

10. Give one example of a source of chemical mutagens.

....

[1]

11. Describe the method that was used to produce Dolly the sheep.

....

....

....

....

....

....

[4]

15

Answers

Section 1 — The Nature and Variety of Organisms

Test 1 — Pages 2-3

1. A *[1 mark]* 2. B *[1 mark]*
3. C *[1 mark]* 4. B *[1 mark]*
5. C *[1 mark]* 6. C *[1 mark]*
7. C *[1 mark]* 8. B *[1 mark]*
9. E.g. influenza virus / tobacco mosaic virus / HIV *[1 mark]*.
10. Any two from: e.g. surface area to volume ratio / concentration gradient / diffusion distance / temperature *[2 marks]*.
11. E.g. stem cells can be transferred from the bone marrow of a healthy person to replace faulty blood cells in the patient who receives them. / Embryonic stem cells could be used to replace faulty cells in sick people/make insulin-producing cells for people with diabetes/make nerve cells for people paralysed by spinal injuries *[1 mark]*.
12. Some of the bonds holding the enzyme together break *[1 mark]*. This changes the shape of the enzyme's active site *[1 mark]*. The enzyme will not be able to bind to the substrate so it won't catalyse the reaction *[1 mark]*.

Test 2 — Pages 4-5

1. C *[1 mark]* 2. A *[1 mark]*
3. C *[1 mark]* 4. B *[1 mark]*
5. B *[1 mark]* 6. A *[1 mark]*
7. B *[1 mark]* 8. A *[1 mark]*
9. E.g. stem cells could be infected with a virus which could be passed on to patients *[1 mark]*.
10. It is the movement of particles against a concentration gradient *[1 mark]* using energy transferred during respiration *[1 mark]*.
11.

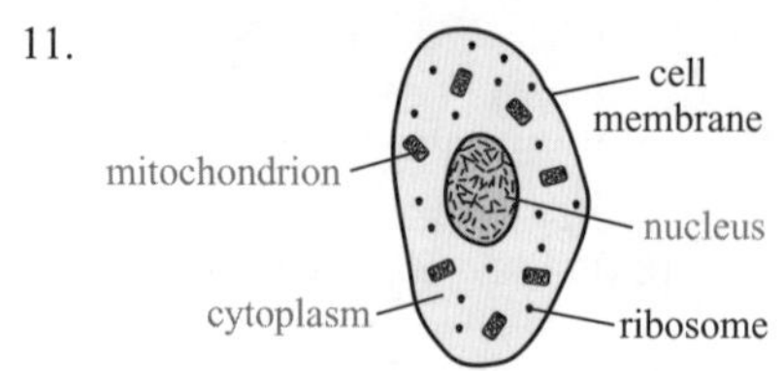

[1 mark for each correct label] Mitochondria are where most of the reactions for aerobic respiration take place *[1 mark]*. The nucleus contains the genetic material that controls the activities of the cell *[1 mark]*.

Test 3 — Pages 6-7

1. C *[1 mark]* 2. A *[1 mark]*
3. B *[1 mark]* 4. C *[1 mark]*
5. C *[1 mark]* 6. A *[1 mark]*
7. B *[1 mark]* 8. B *[1 mark]*
9. Cell differentiation is the process by which cells become specialised for a particular function *[1 mark]*.
10. The rate of diffusion increases *[1 mark]*.
11. If the pH is too high, the pH interferes with the bonds holding the enzyme together *[1 mark]*. This changes the shape of the active site / the enzyme is denatured *[1 mark]*. The enzyme won't be able to bind to the substrate as well, so it won't catalyse the reaction as well and the enzyme's function is reduced *[1 mark]*.
12. The mycelium is the body of some fungi *[1 mark]* made from hyphae/ thread-like structures *[1 mark]*.

Section 2 — Human Nutrition

Test 4 — Pages 8-9

1. A *[1 mark]* 2. B *[1 mark]*
3. A *[1 mark]* 4. B *[1 mark]*
5. C *[1 mark]* 6. A *[1 mark]*
7. A *[1 mark]* 8. A *[1 mark]*
9. Energy in food = $50 \times 16.6 \times 4.2$ = 3486 J *[1 mark]*
10. Any three from: e.g. it's very long. / It has a large surface area. / The villi have a single, permeable layer of surface cells. / The villi have a good blood supply. *[3 marks]*
11.

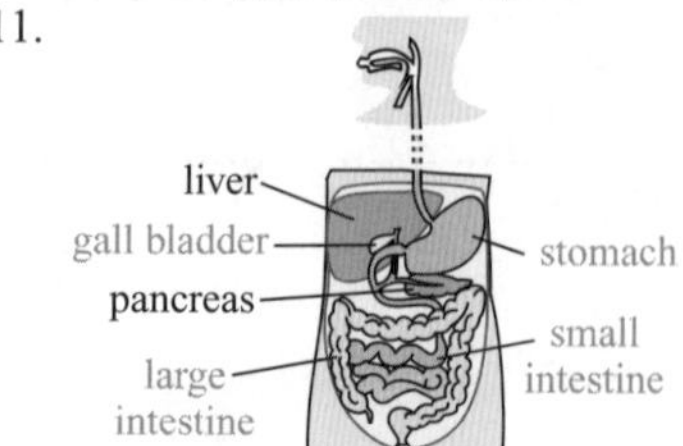

[1 mark for each correct label] The large intestine is where excess water is absorbed from the food *[1 mark]*.

Test 5 — Pages 10-11

1. B *[1 mark]* 2. B *[1 mark]*
3. C *[1 mark]* 4. B *[1 mark]*
5. A *[1 mark]* 6. A *[1 mark]*
7. A *[1 mark]* 8. B *[1 mark]*
9. E.g. the student could insulate the boiling tube *[1 mark]*.
10. The circular muscle around the gut *[1 mark]* contracts in waves to squeeze food through the gut *[1 mark]*.
11. Any two from: carbohydrate / protein / lipid / vitamins / minerals / water / dietary fibre. *[2 marks]*
12. Bile breaks down fat into smaller droplets *[1 mark]*, providing a larger surface area for lipase to work on *[1 mark]*.

Section 3 — Plant Nutrition and Transport

Test 6 — Pages 12-13

1. B *[1 mark]* 2. A *[1 mark]*
3. C *[1 mark]* 4. C *[1 mark]*
5. B *[1 mark]* 6. C *[1 mark]*
7. A *[1 mark]* 8. A *[1 mark]*
9. Because substances only have small distances to travel *[1 mark]*, so the diffusion rate is quick enough *[1 mark]*.

Answers

10. Root hair cells *[1 mark]*.
11. carbon dioxide + water —light energy→ glucose + oxygen
[2 marks for whole equation completed correctly, 1 mark for one or two gaps filled correctly.]
12. It will slow down/stop *[1 mark]* because there will be less/no light present to transfer the energy needed for photosynthesis *[1 mark]*.

Test 7 — Pages 14-15

1. C *[1 mark]* 2. B *[1 mark]*
3. C *[1 mark]* 4. B *[1 mark]*
5. A *[1 mark]* 6. B *[1 mark]*
7. B *[1 mark]* 8. A *[1 mark]*
9. It helps to reduce water loss by evaporation *[1 mark]*.
10. Any two from: light intensity / carbon dioxide concentration / temperature *[2 marks]*.
11. Increasing air movement would increase the rate of transpiration *[1 mark]* because water vapour surrounding the leaf would be swept away *[1 mark]*. This would increase the concentration gradient between water inside and outside the leaf *[1 mark]*, meaning that more water would diffuse out of the leaf *[1 mark]*.

Section 4 — Respiration and Gas Exchange

Test 8 — Pages 16-17

1. B *[1 mark]* 2. A *[1 mark]*
3. B *[1 mark]* 4. C *[1 mark]*
5. A *[1 mark]* 6. B *[1 mark]*
7. A *[1 mark]* 8. C *[1 mark]*
9. E.g. aerobic respiration produces more ATP per glucose molecule than anaerobic respiration *[1 mark]*. Aerobic respiration does not produce lactic acid, unlike anaerobic respiration *[1 mark]*.
10. Photosynthesis leads to the uptake of CO_2, while respiration produces CO_2 *[1 mark]*. Respiration occurs in the dark, but photosynthesis does not *[1 mark]*, so more CO_2 is released into the air than is taken up *[1 mark]*.
11. If the seeds are respiring, the concentration of carbon dioxide in the test tube will increase *[1 mark]*. This will turn the hydrogen-carbonate indicator from red/orange to yellow *[1 mark]*.

Test 9 — Pages 18-19

1. C *[1 mark]* 2. A *[1 mark]*
3. B *[1 mark]* 4. C *[1 mark]*
5. C *[1 mark]* 6. B *[1 mark]*
7. B *[1 mark]* 8. A *[1 mark]*
9. Any one from: e.g. cilia are damaged. / Chest infections are more likely. / Bronchi and bronchioles are irritated. / Causes smoker's cough. / Causes chronic bronchitis. *[1 mark]*
10.

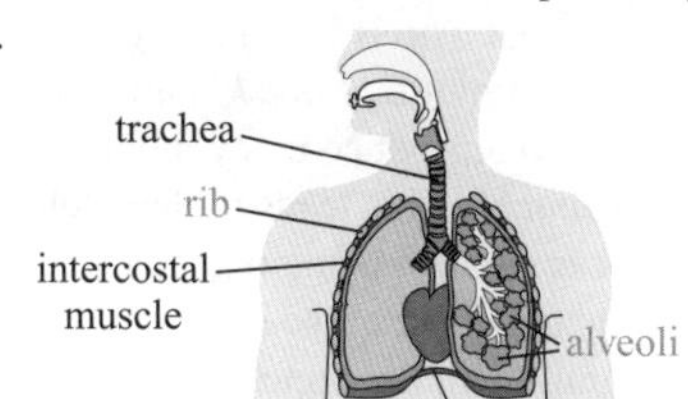

[1 mark for each correct label]

11. The intercostal muscles and the diaphragm relax *[1 mark]* so that the thorax volume decreases and air is forced out of the lungs *[1 mark]*.
12. At night, the stomata don't need to let in CO_2 because photosynthesis is not taking place *[1 mark]*, so the stomata close to reduce water loss *[1 mark]*.

Section 5 — Blood and Organs

Test 10 — Pages 20-21

1. C *[1 mark]* 2. C *[1 mark]*
3. A *[1 mark]* 4. B *[1 mark]*
5. C *[1 mark]* 6. C *[1 mark]*
7. B *[1 mark]* 8. A *[1 mark]*
9. E.g. smoking / being inactive / having a diet high in saturated fat *[1 mark]*.
10. E.g. increases heart rate *[1 mark]*.
11. Any two from: e.g. arteries carry blood away from the heart, whilst veins carry blood to the heart. / Arteries have thick walls, whilst veins have thin walls. / Veins contain valves, but arteries don't. *[2 marks]*
12. The injected dead or inactive pathogens carry antigens *[1 mark]*. The antigens trigger memory cells to be made *[1 mark]*. If live pathogens of the same type appear after that, there will already be memory cells that can produce antibodies quickly and in large numbers *[1 mark]*.

Test 11 — Pages 22-23

1. C *[1 mark]* 2. B *[1 mark]*
3. B *[1 mark]* 4. B *[1 mark]*
5. A *[1 mark]* 6. C *[1 mark]*
7. C *[1 mark]* 8. A *[1 mark]*
9. The left ventricle needs more muscle to pump blood around the whole body *[1 mark]*, whereas the right ventricle only has to pump blood to the lungs *[1 mark]*.
10. Any three from: e.g. red blood cells / white blood cells / platelets / digested food products / CO_2 / urea / hormones / heat energy *[3 marks]*.
11.

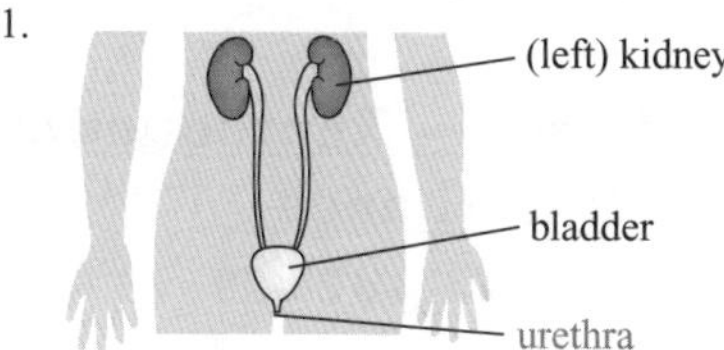

[1 mark for each correct label]

Section 6 — Coordination and Response

Test 12 — Pages 24-25

1. C *[1 mark]* 2. B *[1 mark]*
3. C *[1 mark]* 4. A *[1 mark]*
5. C *[1 mark]* 6. A *[1 mark]*
7. A *[1 mark]* 8. B *[1 mark]*

Answers

9. Electrical impulses are transferred from neurone to neurone by neurotransmitters *[1 mark]* which diffuse across the synapse *[1 mark]*.
10. E.g. it maintains the lining of the uterus *[1 mark]*.
11. E.g. homeostasis is the maintenance of a constant internal environment *[1 mark]*.
12. The ciliary muscles relax / the suspensory ligaments pull tight *[1 mark]*. This results in the lens becoming less curved/thinner *[1 mark]*, so that the lens refracts light by a smaller amount *[1 mark]*.

Test 13 — Pages 26-27

1. B *[1 mark]*
2. B *[1 mark]*
3. C *[1 mark]*
4. A *[1 mark]*
5. C *[1 mark]*
6. A *[1 mark]*
7. C *[1 mark]*
8. A *[1 mark]*
9. (sensory) neurones / nerves *[1 mark]*
10. Receptors detect a stimulus *[1 mark]*.
11. E.g. body water content, body temperature. *[2 marks]*
12. The blood vessels close to the surface of the skin dilate *[1 mark]* so that more blood flows close to the surface of the skin *[1 mark]*. This transfers energy from the body to the environment, helping to lower body temperature *[1 mark]*.

Section 7 — Reproduction and Inheritance

Test 14 — Pages 28-29

1. C *[1 mark]*
2. B *[1 mark]*
3. B *[1 mark]*
4. B *[1 mark]*
5. A *[1 mark]*
6. B *[1 mark]*
7. A *[1 mark]*
8. C *[1 mark]*
9. From its own food reserves *[1 mark]*.
10. The pollen tube grows through the style to the ovule *[1 mark]*, allowing the nucleus from the male gamete to travel to the female gamete *[1 mark]*.
11. Erectile tissue: swells with blood to make the penis erect *[1 mark]*.
Vas deferens: carries sperm from the testis to the urethra *[1 mark]*.
12. Any two from: e.g. for growth / for repair / for cloning / for asexual reproduction *[2 marks]*.

Test 15 — Pages 30-31

1. B *[1 mark]*
2. C *[1 mark]*
3. C *[1 mark]*
4. C *[1 mark]*
5. A *[1 mark]*
6. B *[1 mark]*
7. A *[1 mark]*
8. A *[1 mark]*
9. By gametes being fertilised at random *[1 mark]*.
10. Any two from: e.g. brightly coloured petals / scented flowers / production of nectar / big, sticky pollen grains. *[2 marks]*
11. E.g. a bacterium could develop a random mutation in its DNA that increases its resistance to an antibiotic *[1 mark]*. This means the bacterium is better able to survive in a host who is being treated with that antibiotic *[1 mark]* and so it is able to reproduce many more times *[1 mark]*. This leads to the allele for resistance being passed on to lots of offspring, so it becomes more common in the population over time *[1 mark]*.

Test 16 — Pages 32-33

1. A *[1 mark]*
2. C *[1 mark]*
3. B *[1 mark]*
4. B *[1 mark]*
5. C *[1 mark]*
6. C *[1 mark]*
7. A *[1 mark]*
8. C *[1 mark]*
9. It protects the embryo/fetus against knocks and bumps *[1 mark]*.
10. E.g. some plants send out runners *[1 mark]*. The runners take root at various points and grow into new, identical plants *[1 mark]*.
11.

[1 mark for the gametes' alleles being correct and 1 mark for the offspring's genotypes being correct]
As the cystic fibrosis allele is recessive, for the child to have the disease they will need two recessive alleles *[1 mark]*. The diagram shows that the chance the child will have cystic fibrosis is 25% / 1 in 4 *[1 mark]*.

Test 17 — Pages 34-35

1. A *[1 mark]*
2. A *[1 mark]*
3. A *[1 mark]*
4. C *[1 mark]*
5. B *[1 mark]*
6. C *[1 mark]*
7. A *[1 mark]*
8. B *[1 mark]*
9. A lack of oxygen in the boiling tube with a layer of oil prevented germination *[1 mark]*.
10. The plant will be tall *[1 mark]*, as the tall allele (T) is dominant over the recessive dwarf allele (t) *[1 mark]*.
11. There is genetic variation within a population *[1 mark]* and those individuals with characteristics that make them better adapted to the environment have a better chance of survival *[1 mark]*. They are therefore more likely to survive long enough to breed and pass on the genes responsible for the useful characteristics *[1 mark]*. The beneficial characteristics, therefore, become more common in the population over time *[1 mark]*.

Answers

Section 8 — Ecology and the Environment

Test 18 — Pages 36-37

1. B *[1 mark]* 2. C *[1 mark]*
3. C *[1 mark]* 4. B *[1 mark]*
5. A *[1 mark]* 6. A *[1 mark]*
7. A *[1 mark]* 8. C *[1 mark]*
9. It releases carbon dioxide into the air/water *[1 mark]*.
10. It attaches to haemoglobin in red blood cells *[1 mark]* and prevents them from carrying oxygen *[1 mark]*.
11. Any two from: e.g. by respiration / as heat / in an animal's waste *[2 marks]*.
12. Mean number of limpets per m^2 = $(1 \div 0.25) \times 22 = 88$
    Total population = 88×1800
    = 158 400 limpets
    [2 marks for correct answer, or 1 mark for correct working]

Test 19 — Pages 38-39

1. A *[1 mark]* 2. B *[1 mark]*
3. B *[1 mark]* 4. C *[1 mark]*
5. C *[1 mark]* 6. B *[1 mark]*
7. C *[1 mark]* 8. B *[1 mark]*
9. E.g. biodiversity is the variety of different species of organisms on Earth/within an ecosystem *[1 mark]*.
10. E.g. burning fossil fuels *[1 mark]*, deforestation *[1 mark]*.
11. The excess nitrates cause algae to grow fast and block out the light *[1 mark]*. Plants can't photosynthesise due to lack of light and start to die and decompose *[1 mark]*. With more food available, microorganisms that feed on decomposing plants increase in number and use up oxygen in the water *[1 mark]*. Organisms that need oxygen also die *[1 mark]*.

Test 20 — Pages 40-41

1. C *[1 mark]* 2. B *[1 mark]*
3. B *[1 mark]* 4. B *[1 mark]*
5. C *[1 mark]* 6. A *[1 mark]*
7. C *[1 mark]* 8. B *[1 mark]*
9. The amount of biomass at each stage of a food chain decreases as you go up the chain *[1 mark]*.
10. E.g. a decrease in the availability of food / an increase in the number of predators / competition. *[1 mark]*
11. The number of hawks could decrease *[1 mark]*. The number of snails could increase *[1 mark]*.
12. An increase in the amount of greenhouse gases is causing an enhanced greenhouse effect *[1 mark]* where more heat energy is trapped in the atmosphere *[1 mark]*. This is causing the Earth to heat up, leading to global warming *[1 mark]*.

Section 9 — Use of Biological Resources

Test 21 — Pages 42-43

1. A *[1 mark]* 2. A *[1 mark]*
3. C *[1 mark]* 4. C *[1 mark]*
5. C *[1 mark]* 6. B *[1 mark]*
7. B *[1 mark]* 8. B *[1 mark]*
9. It means genes have transferred from one species to another species *[1 mark]*.
10. By counting how many bubbles are produced in a given period of time *[1 mark]* and by using the rate of carbon dioxide production as an indication of respiration rate *[1 mark]*.
11. Explants are taken from a plant *[1 mark]* and are sterilised *[1 mark]*. They are then grown *in vitro*/ in a nutrient medium *[1 mark]*. After they have grown, the small plants are planted in soil and put into glasshouses *[1 mark]*.

Test 22 — Pages 44-45

1. B *[1 mark]* 2. A *[1 mark]*
3. A *[1 mark]* 4. C *[1 mark]*
5. C *[1 mark]* 6. C *[1 mark]*
7. A *[1 mark]* 8. B *[1 mark]*
9. To kill pests *[1 mark]*.
10. A vector is used to transfer recombinant DNA *[1 mark]* into other cells *[1 mark]*. Example: a (bacterial) plasmid / a virus *[1 mark]*.
11. Tall sunflowers could be cross-bred with other tall sunflowers *[1 mark]*. The tallest resulting sunflowers could be cross-bred again *[1 mark]*. This process could be repeated over several generations to increase the height of the sunflowers further *[1 mark]*.

Mixed Tests for Paper 1

Test 23 — Pages 46-47

1. B *[1 mark]* 2. A *[1 mark]*
3. B *[1 mark]* 4. B *[1 mark]*
5. B *[1 mark]* 6. C *[1 mark]*
7. B *[1 mark]* 8. A *[1 mark]*
9. To prevent backflow of blood in the heart *[1 mark]*.
10. Pulmonary artery *[1 mark]*.
11. Osmosis is the net movement of water molecules across a partially permeable membrane *[1 mark]* from a region of higher water concentration to a region of lower water concentration *[1 mark]*.
12. In multicellular organisms, substances have to travel large distances to reach every cell *[1 mark]*, so direct diffusion would be too slow *[1 mark]*. Transport systems are therefore needed to move substances to and from individual cells quickly *[1 mark]*.

Test 24 — Pages 48-49

1. A *[1 mark]* 2. A *[1 mark]*
3. B *[1 mark]* 4. A *[1 mark]*
5. C *[1 mark]* 6. C *[1 mark]*
7. B *[1 mark]* 8. A *[1 mark]*

Answers

9. E.g. magnesium, nitrates *[2 marks]*.
10. Xylem vessels transport water and mineral ions from the roots to the leaves *[1 mark]*.
11. Exercise increases the amount of carbon dioxide in the blood *[1 mark]*. The increase in blood CO_2 is detected by receptors in the aorta/carotid artery *[1 mark]*, which then send signals to the brain *[1 mark]*. The brain sends signals to the heart, causing it to contract more frequently *[1 mark]*.

Test 25 — Pages 50-51

1. B *[1 mark]* 2. A *[1 mark]*
3. C *[1 mark]* 4. B *[1 mark]*
5. B *[1 mark]* 6. C *[1 mark]*
7. A *[1 mark]* 8. C *[1 mark]*
9. Any two from: e.g. leaves are broad / the palisade layer has lots of chloroplasts / the upper epidermis is transparent / the epidermal tissues are covered with a waxy cuticle / leaves have a network of vascular bundles / there are stomata on the lower surface. *[2 marks]*
10. As electrical impulses *[1 mark]*.
11. Any two from: e.g. both have a cell membrane / both have a nucleus / both have a cytoplasm / both have mitochondria / both have ribosomes. *[2 marks]*
12. Increasing the carbon dioxide concentration could increase the rate of photosynthesis *[1 mark]*, so crops can grow bigger/faster *[1 mark]*.

Test 26 — Pages 52-53

1. C *[1 mark]* 2. B *[1 mark]*
3. B *[1 mark]* 4. A *[1 mark]*
5. C *[1 mark]* 6. B *[1 mark]*
7. C *[1 mark]* 8. A *[1 mark]*
9. E.g. light / gravity / touch / predators / abiotic stress. *[1 mark]*
10. Fallopian tube: carries the ovum from the ovary to the uterus *[1 mark]*.
    Endometrium: provides a good blood supply for implantation of an embryo *[1 mark]*.
11. Any two from: e.g. nerves send faster messages than hormones. / Nervous responses last for a shorter time than hormonal responses. / Nerves act on a very precise area, while hormones act in a more general way. *[2 marks]*
12. Any two from: e.g. they produce large amounts of pollen grains / they have long filaments / they have large/feathery stigmas. *[2 marks]*

Mixed Tests for Paper 2

Test 27 — Pages 54-55

1. B *[1 mark]* 2. C *[1 mark]*
3. B *[1 mark]* 4. A *[1 mark]*
5. C *[1 mark]* 6. B *[1 mark]*
7. A *[1 mark]* 8. A *[1 mark]*
9. Proximal convoluted tubule *[1 mark]*.
10. Secretion of extracellular enzymes to dissolve food *[1 mark]* so that the nutrients can then be absorbed *[1 mark]*.
11. For a greater concentration gradient — it increases the rate of diffusion *[1 mark]*. For a greater distance — it decreases the rate of diffusion *[1 mark]*.
12. Pulmonary vein *[1 mark]*
    Aorta *[1 mark]*

Test 28 — Pages 56-57

1. A *[1 mark]* 2. B *[1 mark]*
3. C *[1 mark]* 4. B *[1 mark]*
5. A *[1 mark]* 6. B *[1 mark]*
7. A *[1 mark]* 8. B *[1 mark]*
9. Proteins and blood cells are too large *[1 mark]* to pass through the membrane between the blood vessels in the glomerulus and the Bowman's capsule *[1 mark]*.
10. More ADH is released by the pituitary gland *[1 mark]* so that the kidneys reabsorb more water / the collecting ducts become more permeable to water *[1 mark]*.
11. ff *[1 mark]*.
    100% *[1 mark]*.
12. Potometer *[1 mark]*.

Test 29 — Pages 58-59

1. A *[1 mark]* 2. C *[1 mark]*
3. A *[1 mark]* 4. C *[1 mark]*
5. B *[1 mark]* 6. A *[1 mark]*
7. C *[1 mark]* 8. B *[1 mark]*
9. E.g. to maximise the amount of energy they get from their food *[1 mark]*.
10. When the air is more humid, there is less of a difference in water content between the air inside and the air outside the leaf / the concentration gradient is lower *[1 mark]*. Water therefore diffuses more slowly out of the leaf *[1 mark]*.
11. When trees are cut down and burnt, the stored carbon is released as carbon dioxide *[1 mark]* and the amount of carbon dioxide in the atmosphere increases *[1 mark]*. Fewer trees also means less oxygen is released from photosynthesis *[1 mark]*, causing the amount of oxygen in the atmosphere to drop *[1 mark]*.

Test 30 — Pages 60-61

1. B *[1 mark]* 2. A *[1 mark]*
3. B *[1 mark]* 4. C *[1 mark]*
5. A *[1 mark]* 6. C *[1 mark]*
7. B *[1 mark]* 8. C *[1 mark]*
9. E.g. temperature *[1 mark]*.
   By using a water bath / an electric heater. *[1 mark]*
10. E.g. tobacco *[1 mark]*.
11. The nucleus of a sheep's egg cell was removed / an enucleated cell was produced from a sheep's egg cell *[1 mark]*. A diploid nucleus from a mature sheep was inserted in its place *[1 mark]*. The cell was stimulated to divide by mitosis *[1 mark]* and then implanted into the uterus of another sheep to develop *[1 mark]*.